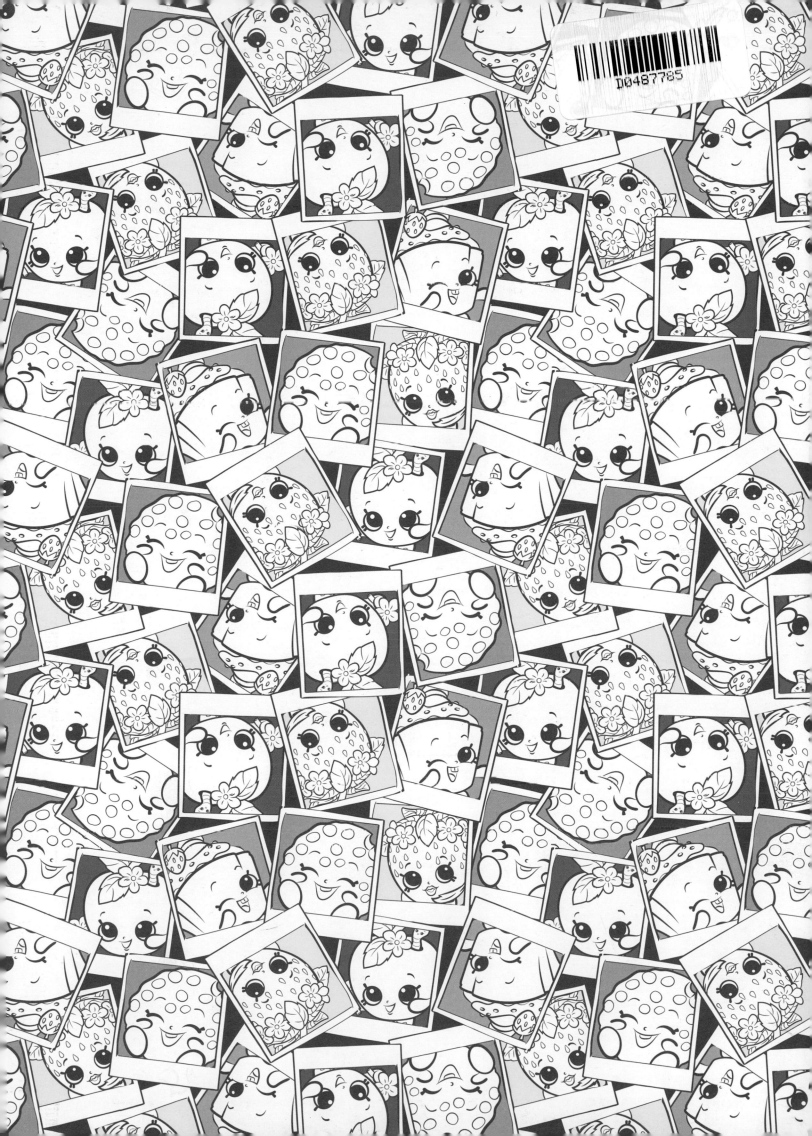

SHOPKINS: 2017

A CENTUM BOOK 9781910917220

Published in Great Britain by Centum Books Ltd

This edition published 2016

1 3 5 7 9 10 8 6 4 2

Centum Books Ltd, 20 Devon Square, Newton Abbot, Devon TQ12 2HR, UK

books@centumbooksltd.co.uk

CENTUM BOOKS Limited Reg. No. 07641486

A CIP catalogue record for this book is available from the British Library

Printed in China

# Shopkins™

Once you shop...You can't stop!

## 2017

This **SHOPKINS™** book belongs to:

........................................................

centum

# WHAT'S INSIDE?

#SPKFAN!

#APPLE_BLOSSOM

#D'LISH_DONUT

#KOOKY_COOKIE

SPK

#SNEAKY_WEDGE

# WELCOME TO SHOPVILLE!

Shopkins collectors, get ready for VIP access to an adorable adventure! All your favourite characters from across the Seasons are waiting for you, from Apple Blossom to Kooky Cookie, Poppy Corn to Cupcake Chic, Taco Terrie to Sneaky Sally … and loads more. (Miss Pressy asked for a special mention!)

And all the Shoppies are here too! Jessicake, Popette, Bubbleisha, Donatina and the totally gorgeous, minty-haired Peppa-Mint have loads of styling and friendship games, just for you.

Finally, don't forget the super-cute and totally awesome Petkins, who definitely want to play!

## ONCE YOU SHOP ...
## YOU CAN'T STOP

# LOOK FOR THE LIMITED EDITION SHOPKINS!

Can you find these oh-so-special Season 4 Shopkins hiding in this book? Each one appears in a yellow star. Tick them off here as you find them!

 Pretty Puff ☐      Frenchy Perfume ☐      Gemma Bottle ☐

 Pretty Bow Kay ☐      Sparkly Spritz ☐      Sally Scent ☐

# BLIND BAG

Which fruity friends are hiding inside these shoppers?
Write their names before they pop right out!

**1**

\_ \_ \_ \_ \_   \_ \_ \_ \_ \_

**2**

\_ \_ \_ \_ \_ \_   \_ \_ \_ \_ \_ \_

**3**

\_ \_ \_ \_ \_

**4**

\_ \_ \_ \_ \_   \_ \_ \_ \_ \_ \_

**5**

\_ \_ \_ \_   \_ \_ \_ \_

**6**

\_ \_ \_ \_ \_ \_   \_ \_ \_ \_ \_ \_ \_

# MYSTERY SHOPKIN

Ooh, who is it? Cross out all of the letter pairs, then unscramble the
remaining letters to reveal a citrus-bright Shopkin from Season 2.

R  T  J  Y  F  A  P

L  S  N  S  P  T  E

C  F  G  L  I  C  U

O

\_ \_ \_ \_ \_ \_   \_ \_ \_ \_ \_

ANSWERS ON PAGE 61

# SHOPKIN SHADOWS

## Can you work out who these cute shadows belong to?

1

2

3

_____  _____  _____

4

5

6

I'll tell you a secret – they're all from Season 3, like me!

_____  _____  _____

# AISLE BE QUICK!

Hurry, it's nearly closing time and the Shopkins need to get back to their own aisles. Which route should each character take?

FRUIT & VEG

DAIRY

HEALTH & BEAUTY

# MEET SEASON 1

## DAIRY

**CHEE ZEE**
A confident performer who loves taking centre stage – and is a little bit crackers!
♥s rapping with his BFFs.

**GOOGY**
Clumsy and shy, his friends try to get him to come out of his shell.
♥s juggling!

**SPILT MILK**
A bit of a klutz and a born risk-taker, she likes to stir things up.
♥s skimming through comic books.

**SWISS MISS**
A hilarious jokester and stand-up comedian.
♥s cheesy jokes!

## BAKERY

**KOOKY COOKIE**
Really shy and sensitive, her friends encourage her to try new things.
♥s thinking outside the cookie jar.

**D'LISH DONUT**
Super sweet but with a competitive edge.
♥s trying for the perfect hole-in-one.

**MINI MUFFIN**
Sweet inside and out, with a lot of energy.
♥s mornings – she's an early riser!

**BREAD HEAD**
Independent and confident and a bit of a chatterbox.
♥s chatting on the phone!

**APPLE BLOSSOM**
An adventurer with big dreams and kind to the core.
♥s going on adventures!

**STRAWBERRY KISS**
A daydreamer with a huge imagination and often away with the fairies!
♥s writing poetry.

**MELONIE PIPS**
Refreshing to be around. Likes to get involved and always loves a slice of the action!
♥s dancing to 'Pip-Hop' music!

## FRUIT & VEG

**POSH PEAR**
She's a bit spoilt, but is a good listener and friendly.
♥s playing cards.

**PINEAPPLE CRUSH**
Silly and fun and a lover of the sun!
♥s surfing and sunbaking.

**MISS MUSHY MOO**
A bit of a softy but with a good head on her shoulders.
♥s making mud pies!

### SODA POPS
Super bubbly and sweet, she adds fizz to any party.

♥ s shaking it on the dance floor!

### WOBBLES
A bit klutzy and a worry wart, but she loves to jiggle on the dance floor.

♥ s hip hop dancing!

### RAINBOW BITE
Optimistic and adventurous, she always looks on the positive side of life.

♥ s painting!

### WISHES
A real party starter and a bit of an attention seeker.

♥ s singing for anyone who'll listen!

### FAIRY CRUMBS
Cute and colourful with a love for all things pink and purple.

♥ s parties!

### PRETZ-ELLE
A little scatter-brained, but also cheeky and charming.

♥ s gymnastics!

### CHEEZEY B
A Shopkin who never stops rhyming.

♥ s rapping with his BFFs!

## PANTRY

### PEPPE PEPPER
Always sneezing! He's clever and kind and a bit of a daredevil.

♥ s spicing things up!

### SALLY SHAKES
She adds some fun and flavour to any party.

♥ s rock climbing!

### SUGAR LUMP
A real sweety who gets along with everyone.

♥ s perfecting the ultimate cup of tea!

### BREAKY CRUNCH
Full of energy and ready to go at a moment's notice.

♥ s working out!

### GRAN JAM
Caring, gentle and the mother of the group.

♥ s knitting and jamming on the ukulele!

### TOMMY KETCHUP
Extremely cheeky and always wants to be a part of everything.

♥ s trolley riding!

# MEET SEASON 1

## HEALTH & BEAUTY

**LIPPY LIPS**
A fashionista with sassy style, and maybe a bit bossy!
♥s shopping, of course!

**SHAMPY**
We never know if she's Silky or Shampy!
♥s smelling fresh!

**SILKY**
Partners-in-crime with Shampy, with a great sense of style!
♥s swimming!

**SCRUBS**
Chatty and always grinning, she loves to make people smile.
♥s tubing!

**POLLY POLISH**
A fashion risk-taker who's always trying new colours.
♥s telling the unvarnished truth!

## FROZEN

**COOL CUBE**
A bit of a snow bunny, who hates hot weather.
♥s snowboarding and sledging!

**ICE CREAM DREAM**
Scoops of fun but maybe a bit of a headache at times.
♥s building igloos!

**SNOW CRUSH**
A snowkin builder extraordinaire.
♥s snowkin building and curling.

**POPSI COOL**
Cold on the outside but warm and gooey on the inside!
♥s ice skating.

**YO-CHI**
Well cultured and different each day.
♥s swirling around the dance floor!

**FREEZY PEAZY**
Super cool and the best rapper in the pod.
♥s rapping with his BFFs!

**CHEEKY CHOCOLATE**
Always laughing, having fun and never afraid to get dirty.
♥s playing pranks!

**LOLLI POPPINS**
As sweet as can be! She loves smiling and making Shopkins laugh.
♥s hairdressing!

**BUBBLES**
She can talk a LOT, but is really kind and caring.
♥s singing a tune!

**LE'QUORICE**
She's old fashioned but still the life of any party.
♥s playing hopscotch!

**CANDY KISSES**
Romantic and smooth, although he hasn't had a date just yet.
♥s swriting poetry!

**JELLY B**
Full of beans with a colourful personality.
♥s skipping!

## SWEET TREATS

### CUPCAKE QUEEN

Super sweet and a keeper of the peace.

♥s hosting grand balls!

### BUTTERCUP

Mellow and yellow but cute enough to melt any hearts.

♥s his great taste!

### TIN'A'TUNA

He often thinks there's something fishy going on and loves canned applause.

♥s swimming upstream.

### TWINKY WINKS

She says Shopkins are the cream of the crop but can sponge off her friends a bit.

♥s surprising her friends!

### PAPA TOMATO

A story teller who adds flavour to everything he does.

♥s chatting with pals on the vine.

### SUNNY SCREEN

Over protective and a bit of a worry wart.

♥s nice weather – the hotter, the better!

## EXCLUSIVES

### SPONGECAKE

A Shopkin who loves to party! She takes the cake when it comes to being the most colorful character in the room!

♥s playing party games.

### LA' LOTION

A beautiful looking Shopkin who really takes care of herself... She's always giving out beauty advice.

♥s reading gossip magazines.

### COCO NUTTY

A little kooky and a lot nutty, but very easy going and relaxed. Always dreaming about lying under a palm tree!

♥s sunbaking.

### MARGARINA

Super helpful! A real softy who likes to spread herself around and help where she can.

♥s buttering up her friends.

### ROLLY ROLL

A Shopkin who loves food and will never let you down. Always by your side if there's a plate of food around!

♥s roller skating.

### PUMPKINELLA

She may not look it but she's no ordinary pumpkin. Pumpkinella loves going to Royal Balls, but is never out after midnight!

♥s going on carriage rides.

### HOT APPLE PIE

Warm on the inside and sweet on the outside. Sometimes she's too hot to handle!

♥s baking for her friends.

### CURLY FRIES

A quite and shy little fry. Would much rather curl up with a good book than go out and play!

♥s watching Shirley Temple Movies.

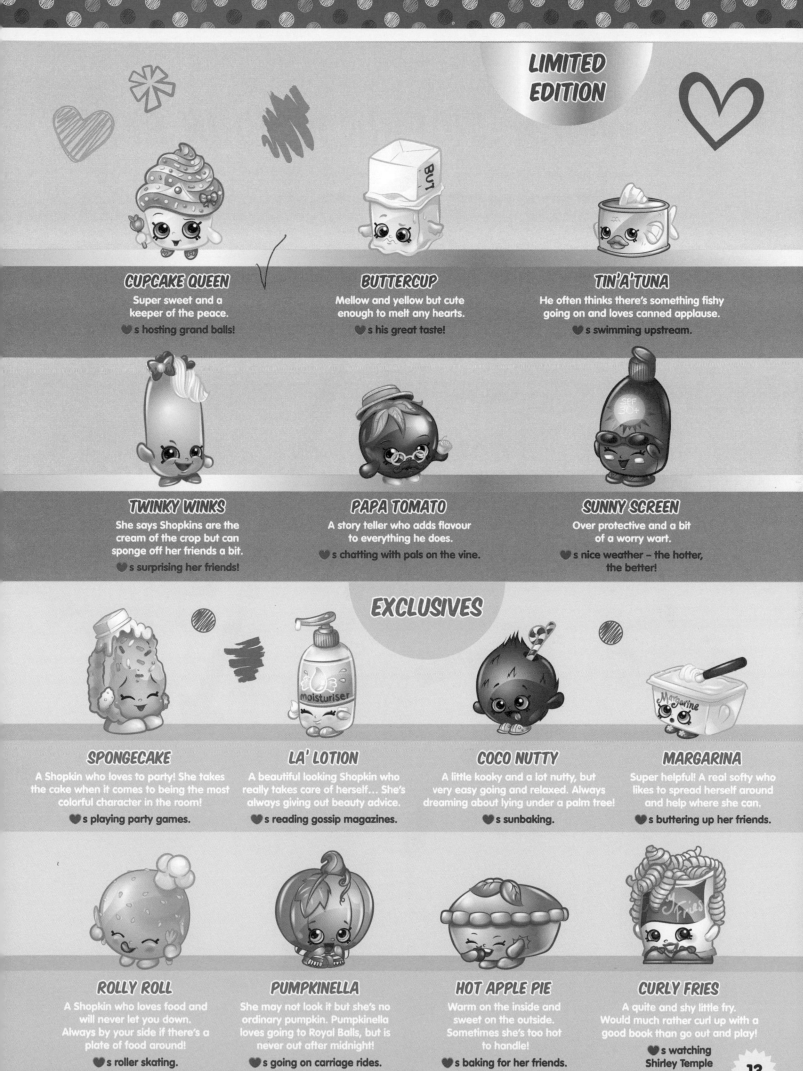

# WHICH SHOPKIN IS YOUR BFF?

How adorable are the Season 4 characters? Which one would you be hanging out in the aisles with? Try this fun quiz to find out.

YOUR BFF IS

PETA PLANT!

YOUR BFF IS

ICE CREAM QUEEN!

YOUR BFF IS

MISS PRESSY!

Is spring better than autumn?

Do you like trying new hairstyles?

YES

NO

YES

YES

Is your favourite flower pink?

START HERE
Is your fave Shopkin a Petkin?

NO

NO

YES

Are savoury snacks better than sweet?

Are pink and purple just the BEST?

NO

NO

YES

YES

Do you love surprises?

NO

Can you ever eat too much ice cream?

YES

YES

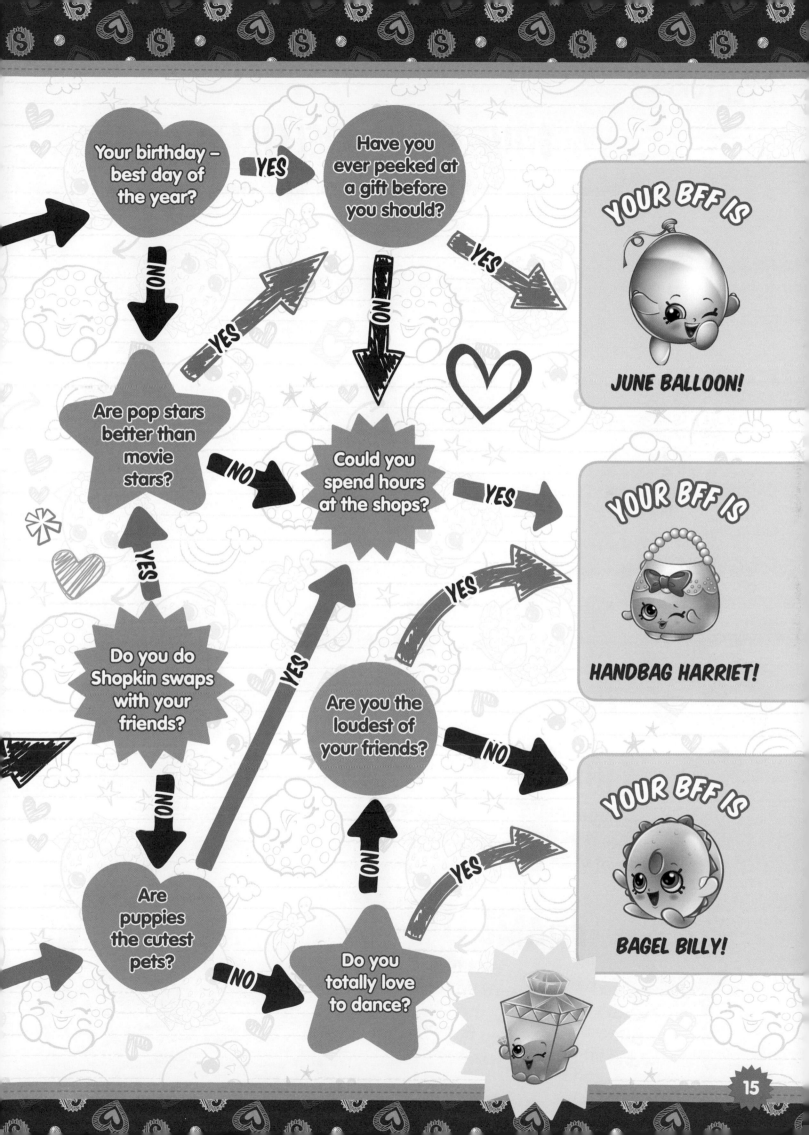

Your birthday – best day of the year?

**YES** →

Have you ever peeked at a gift before you should?

**YES** → YOUR BFF IS JUNE BALLOON!

**NO** ↓

Are pop stars better than movie stars?

**YES** ↗

**NO** →

Could you spend hours at the shops?

**YES** → YOUR BFF IS HANDBAG HARRIET!

**NO** ↓

Do you do Shopkin swaps with your friends?

**YES** ↑

**YES** ↗

**NO** ↓

Are you the loudest of your friends?

**NO** → 

**YES** → YOUR BFF IS BAGEL BILLY!

Are puppies the cutest pets?

**NO** →

Do you totally love to dance?

**NO** ↑

15

# LOVE YOUR #SELFIE!

Check out Smarty Phone's top tips for super-cute selfies.

BESTIES FOR LIFE!

## LIGHT IT UP

Natural light from a window or outdoors is best. Make sure the sun is in front of you to avoid shadows.

## FRAME IT

Pause before you click to check out what's in the picture. Move your camera around for the best shot, and lift it up high to fit more in. You can crop it after, too.

LET'S GET IT POPPIN'

YEAH!

# GO PROP-TASTIC!

You can buy fun prop kits or, even better, make your own. Challenge your buddies to come up with a prop that says something about them, then snap away!

**WHAT'S NOT TO LOVE!?**

SPK
xox

GIRLS' DAY OUT

SPK

## STICK WITH IT!

If you want to fit in more BFFs or a cool background, you'll need a selfie stick. It has a clamp to hold your camera or phone and an extendable arm with a button on the end. Just lift and click!

## BE SUPER SILLY

Smiley pics are nice, but funny pics are SO awesome! Who can take the most fabulously funny selfie?

## FUN WITH FILTERS

Add cool effects at the touch of a button! There are lots of free apps that can spice up your snaps.

ANSWERS ON
PAGE 61

# TROLLEY DASH

It's a busy day in Shopsville! Grab your favourite Shopkins by
drawing lines to put them into the correct baskets.

WHICH SHOPKIN
BELONGS IN
ANOTHER AISLE?
CIRCLE HER.

FRUIT & VEG          PARTY          BAKERY

18

I'M KIND OF A BIG DEAL.

# D'LISH DRAWING

This GLAZED SWEETIE is iced to perfection! Copy D'Lish Donut into the grid below square by square.

Now sprinkle her with COLOUR.

# WHO'S YOUR SHOPPIE TWIN?

## WHICH SUPER-CUTE SHOPPIE ARE YOU MOST LIKE?
## TICK THE WORDS AND PHRASES THAT ARE SO YOU.

- [ ] I ♥ bubble gum.
- [ ] Everything should be pink.
- [ ] Okay, I get moody.
- [ ] Friends should share secrets.
- [ ] Plaits are super-cute.

- [ ] Popcorn is totally yum.
- [ ] It's true ... I'm loud.
- [ ] Every moment needs a selfie.
- [ ] Movies are my life.
- [ ] I can't stop talking.

- [ ] Always smiling.
- [ ] I could shop forever.
- [ ] I love to treat my pets.
- [ ] Cupcakes = awesome.
- [ ] Fashion bows are cute.

- [ ] Daydream all day.
- [ ] Donuts = amazing.
- [ ] Sweet to friends? Always.
- [ ] I'm always the agony aunt.
- [ ] Fun comes first.

- [ ] A BIT of a drama queen.
- [ ] Super-shy? That's me.
- [ ] My BFFs are awesome.
- [ ] I always get the goss.
- [ ] Ice cream is the BEST.

# COUNT UP YOUR ANSWERS IN EACH COLOUR TO FIND OUT YOUR SHOPPIE MATCH!

Blue ☐    Yellow ☐    Pink ☐    Green ☐    Purple ☐

## MOSTLY BLUE
Your Shoppie twin is ...
### JESSICAKE
You're a cupcake cutie and a real sweetie. Smart and sensible, you love to treat your friends to cute handmade gifts.

## MOSTLY YELLOW
Your Shoppie twin is ...
### POPETTE
You're a bowl lot of fun! Loud and loveable, your favourite thing to do is to chill out with friends and a good movie.

## MOSTLY GREEN
Your Shoppie twin is ...
### PEPPA-MINT
You may sometimes lose your cool, but that's because you're so warm-hearted. And you always have the scoop on the gossip!

## MOSTLY PINK
Your Shoppie twin is ...
### BUBBLEISHA
You're bubble trouble! You're strong-willed and full of opinions, but your besties know just how sweet you can be.

## MOSTLY PURPLE
Your Shoppie twin is ...
### DONATINA
You're happy-dough-lucky! You may be a bit of a daydreamer, but when your friends need you, you're always around.

# MEET SEASON 2

### JUICY ORANGE

Maybe a little pushy, she can put the squeeze on you.

♥ s keeping juicy secrets!

### CORNY COB

His friends think he's a bit corny – but you'd have to 'husk' them about that!

♥ s doing puzzles and maizes.

### DIPPY AVOCADO

A true greenie who likes to spread himself around.

♥ s taking a dip on a hot day.

### CHLOE FLOWER

A bit of a hippy and all about 'flower power'. Never 'leafs' her friends behind.

♥ s leafing through the newspaper.

### SILLY CHILLI

Some friends think he comes across as cold, but he's really just a little chilli!

♥ s eating very HOT dogs.

### SNEAKY WEDGE

Footloose and fancy-free, but gets a little tongue-tied now and then.

♥ s hanging out in the gym.

### BETTY BOOT

Gets her kicks riding high in the saddle, she's the wildest boot in the West.

♥ s boot scootin'!

### BUN BUN SLIPPER

A bit of a snoozy head who is always ready for bed. She'd better hop to it!

♥ s doing the bunny hop dance.

## SHOES

### PROMMY

High-spirited and never flat, she is known for her fabulous style.

♥ s kicking up her heels!

### HEELS

Always a hard worker, she buckles down and gets on with things.

♥ s tap dancing!

## SWEET TREATS

**POPPY CORN**

She knows how to bag a bargain and can shop 'til she pops!

♥s going to the movies.

**ICE-CREAM DREAM**

A little bit drippy but never loses her cool. She's cool, cone and collected!

♥s chilling out in her own cone.

**WAFFLE SUE**

A total chatterbox who loves to stay toasty warm!

♥s waffling on about anything.

**PAMELA PANCAKE**

Stacks of fun! Overflowing with sweetness, but never too syrupy.

♥s flipping out in the diving pool.

**MINNIE MINTIE**

A breath of fresh air! She's cool to be around, with hugs and kisses for everyone.

♥s yoga and deep breathing.

**TOASTY POP**

He never has a stale idea and always pops up with new stuff.

♥s throwing parties and giving toasts!

**LANA LAMP**

Loves light-hearted jokes and coming up with bright ideas.

♥s reading in bed.

**BRENDA BLENDER**

A smooth operator who sometimes stirs up trouble.

♥s mixing with her friends.

## HOMEWARES

**ZAPPY MICROWAVE**

A real fast thinker who wants everything done yesterday!

♥s speed-reading.

**SIZZLES**

Warm-hearted rather than hot-tempered, she loves to steam through her jobs!

♥s riding on steam trains.

23

## BAKERY

### CUPCAKE CHIC

A fun-filled girl whose cup is always overflowing with sweet thoughts!

♥ s baking up new ideas to treat her friends!

### PECANNA PIE

A bit nutty in the head but a real sweetheart inside!

♥ s going to the ballet, especially 'The Nutcracker'.

### MARY MERINGUE

Sweet and fluffy, she always has her head in the clouds.

♥ s whipping up treats!

### CARRIE CARROT CAKE

Sweet but a little nutty. People say she has a 24-carrot heart of gold!

♥ s horse riding!

### SLICK BREADSTICK

Crusty on the outside, but warm on the inside!

♥ s lunching in a French café.

### FIFI FRUIT TART

A bit of a fruit loop, who likes to mix things up!

♥ s catching some sun so she's just ripe.

### DUM MEE MEE

A peacekeeper who is no dummy when it comes to stopping tears.

♥ s rocking out with babies.

### BABY PUFF

A sweet-smelling Shopkin who never makes rash decisions!

♥ s finding shapes in the clouds.

### NAPPY DEE

A hard worker in any weather, wet or dry, night or day! It's a big job for a little nappy!

♥ s dancing her pants off!

## BABY

### DRIBBLES

When she hears a cry for help, this little squirt can save the day!

♥ s taking nice warm baths.

### SIPPY SIPS

Never spills a secret and likes to be held tight.

♥ s singing lullabies.

### BABY SWIPES

A real clean machine, she keeps things shiny from top to bottom.

♥ s swiping out in a wave.

### CORNELL MUSTARD
A little squirt with big flavour who can make any hot dog a little hotter.

❤s solving mysteries.

### AL FOIL
Strong and protective, but he can get torn between friends.

❤s wrapping with his friends.

### FASTA PASTA
A great friend to twirl around with, and totally unspaghettable!

❤s shooting hoops with meatballs.

### FI FI FLOUR
A little bit messy to be around, but she'll help anybody in a sticky situation.

❤s half-baked ideas!

### HONEEEY
She can bee charming, she can bee helpful, and she loves to bee sweet!

❤s the spelling bee and catching flies.

## CLEANING & LAUNDRY

### MOLLY MOPS
Buckets of fun! She's a real hard worker with a shiny personality.

❤s playing mopscotch.

### SQUEAKY CLEAN
Honest and clean-cut, she's in a 'glass' of her own!

❤s writing poetry.

### SWEEPS
Don't just brush past Sweeps, she'll be your friend from dust 'til dawn!

❤s brushing up on her schooling.

### WENDY WASHER
A truthful Shopkin who lays it on the line. She's a clean-living girl!

❤s spin cycle classes at the gym.

### LEAFY
A girl who knows her roll in life, she always feels flushed with success!

❤s unwinding with a good magazine.

### MARSHA MELLOW
A real softie who doesn't like the heat!

❤s camping out around the fire.

### RUB-A-GLOVE
The Queen of Clean when it comes to dishing up sparkling plates.

❤s water sports.

### LENNY LIME
Born to please with just a little squeeze!

❤s sipping on a soda.

**LIMITED EDITION**

### LEE TEA
She gets stronger with time and loves a dip in a hot tub.

❤s handbags, shoulder bags and tea bags.

### DONNA DONUT
Every day is a great day with Donna, but the best are Fry-Days.

❤s a hole lot of stuff!

### ANGIE ANKLE BOOT
Known for taking problems in her stride, and never too big for her boots.

❤s disco dancing.

# DAZZLING DOT-TO-DOT

### Which beautiful Shopkin loves to leave her mark wherever she goes? Join the dots to find out.

Delight this fashionista with a gloss of **HOT PINK** when you finish.

SPK
xOx

26

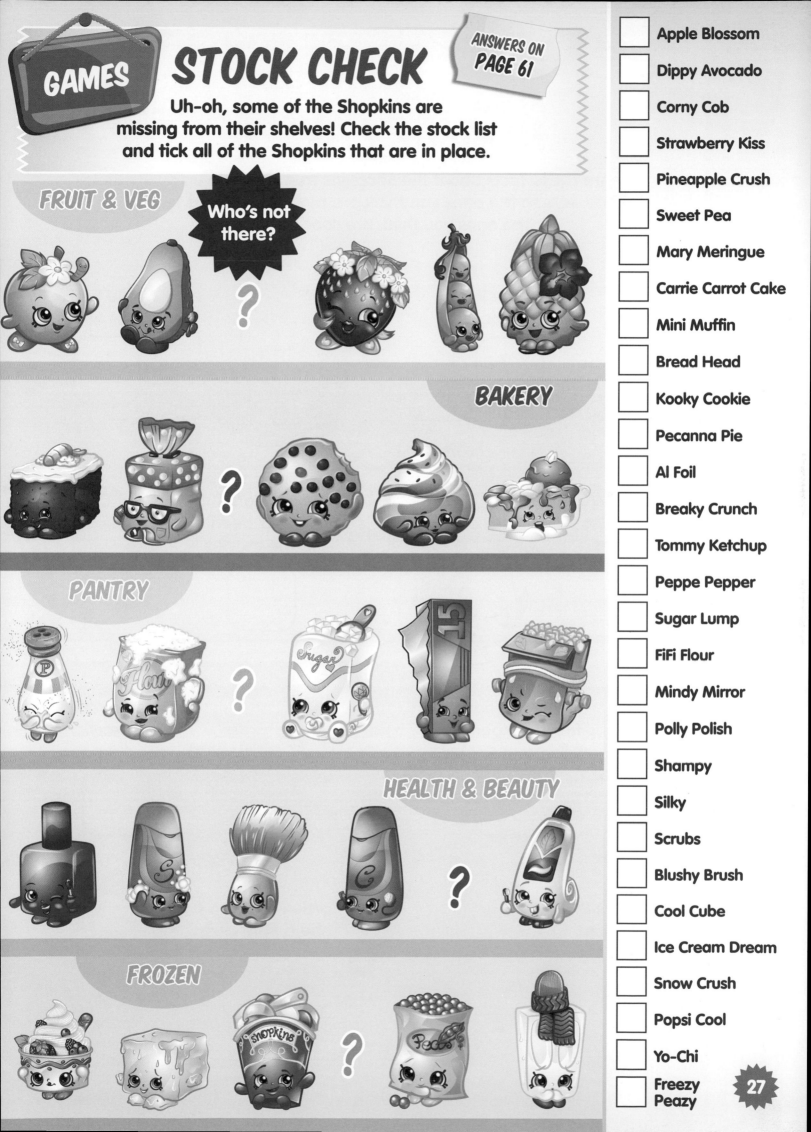

# GAMES

# STOCK CHECK

ANSWERS ON PAGE 61

Uh-oh, some of the Shopkins are missing from their shelves! Check the stock list and tick all of the Shopkins that are in place.

## FRUIT & VEG

**Who's not there?**

?

## BAKERY

?

## PANTRY

?

## HEALTH & BEAUTY

?

## FROZEN

?

- [ ] Apple Blossom
- [ ] Dippy Avocado
- [ ] Corny Cob
- [ ] Strawberry Kiss
- [ ] Pineapple Crush
- [ ] Sweet Pea
- [ ] Mary Meringue
- [ ] Carrie Carrot Cake
- [ ] Mini Muffin
- [ ] Bread Head
- [ ] Kooky Cookie
- [ ] Pecanna Pie
- [ ] Al Foil
- [ ] Breaky Crunch
- [ ] Tommy Ketchup
- [ ] Peppe Pepper
- [ ] Sugar Lump
- [ ] FiFi Flour
- [ ] Mindy Mirror
- [ ] Polly Polish
- [ ] Shampy
- [ ] Silky
- [ ] Scrubs
- [ ] Blushy Brush
- [ ] Cool Cube
- [ ] Ice Cream Dream
- [ ] Snow Crush
- [ ] Popsi Cool
- [ ] Yo-Chi
- [ ] Freezy Peazy

# REAL OR FAKE?

Are these facts about the Shopkins true or made up?
Add ticks to the ones you think are real, and crosses to
the ones you think are sooo fake.

Cool Cube loves
winter sports.

1

Waffle Sue is
super quiet.

2

Corny Cob loves
doing puzzles
and maizes.

3

Poppy Corn has
never been
to the movies.

4

Sneaky Wedge's
favourite game is
'Hide and Sneak'.

5

Zappy Microwave
is an excellent
speed reader.

6

Penny Pencil's BFF
is Candy Apple.

7

Cornell Mustard can
be a little chilly.

8

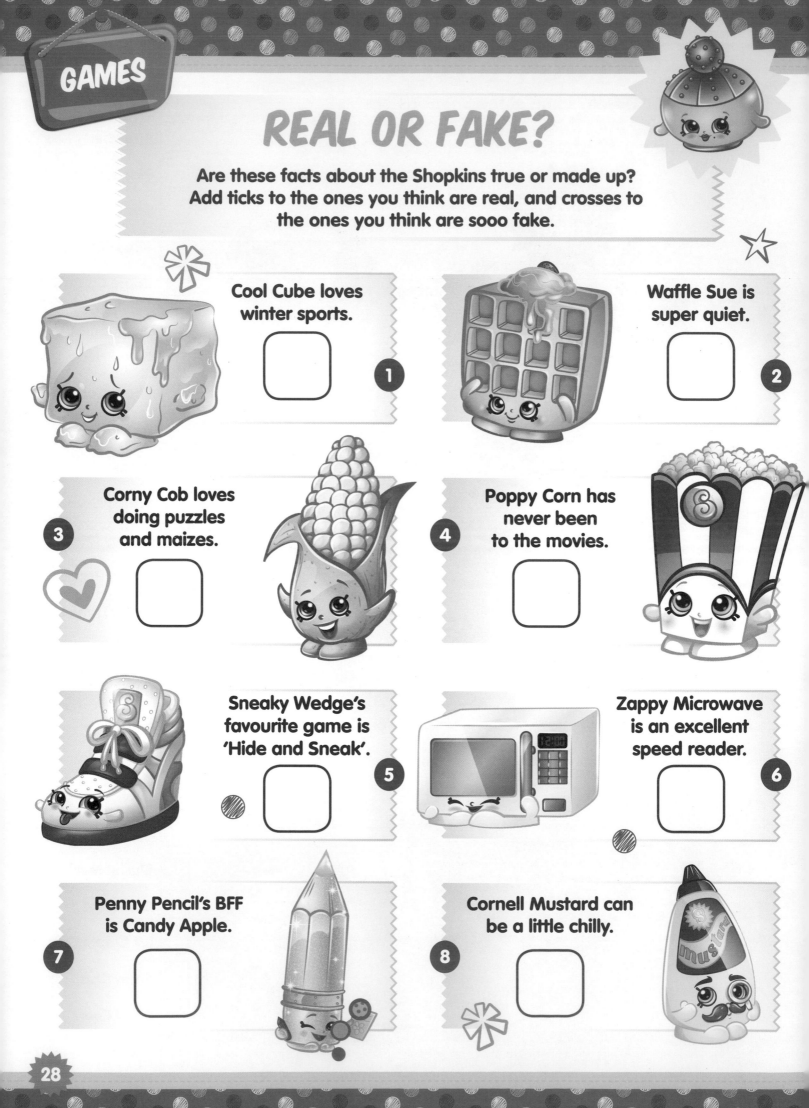

ANSWERS ON PAGE 61

# SHOPVILLE SEARCH

Can you find all of the super Shopkins words
in the wordsearch?

| J | A | T | R | O | L | L | E | Y | B |
|---|---|---|---|---|---|---|---|---|---|
| T | S | Z | A | L | F | O | I | L | A |
| I | U | I | S | V | I | M | P | L | G |
| L | T | P | A | N | T | R | Y | E | C |
| L | S | T | O | C | K | V | V | A | H |
| B | A | K | E | R | Y | Q | Q | F | A |
| R | A | I | B | N | K | Z | Q | Y | T |
| M | A | C | C | A | R | O | O | N | T |
| C | H | E | C | K | O | U | T | Y | E |
| D | A | I | R | Y | U | W | V | Q | R |

| TROLLEY | TILL | DAIRY |
|---------|------|-------|
| BAG | STOCK | PANTRY |
| CHECKOUT | BAKERY | |

**1**

— — — — — — — —

Write the
names of these
cute Season 2
characters.

**2**

— — — — — —

**3**

— — — — — — — — —

Can you find
us in the
grid, too?

**4**

— — — — —

# SHOPKINS MATCH

## EACH SHOPPIE HAS HER OWN ADORABLE SHOPKIN BESTIES. CAN YOU DRAW LINES TO MATCH THE SHOPPIES TO THEIR TWO SHOPKINS?

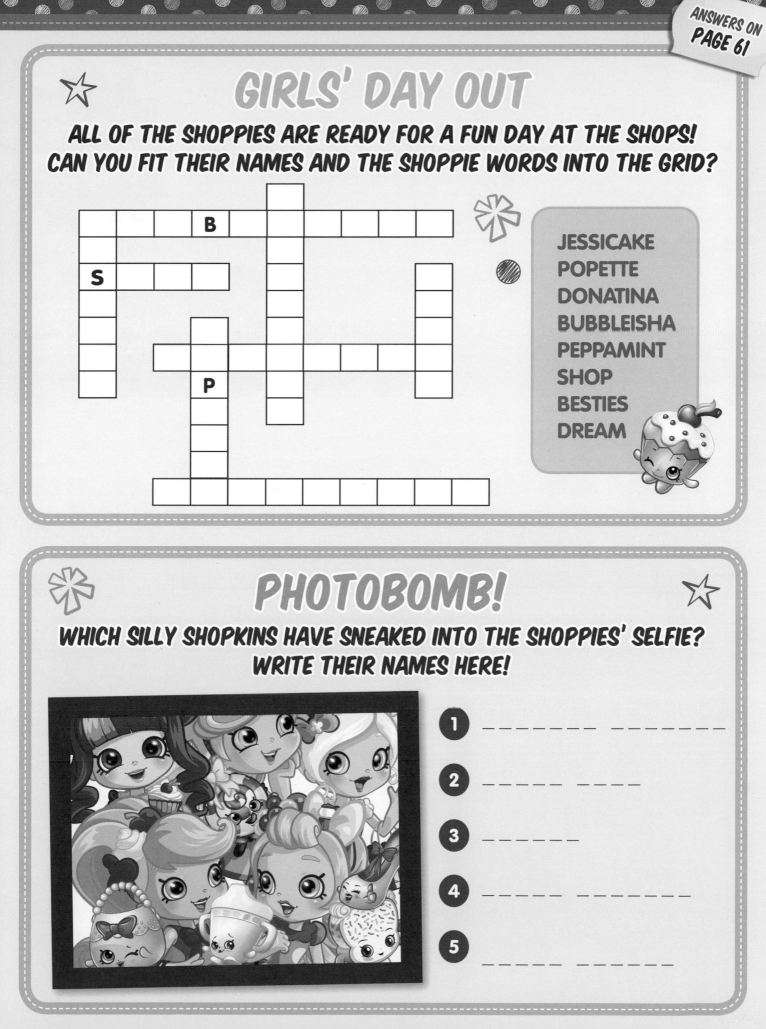

# GIRLS' DAY OUT

ALL OF THE SHOPPIES ARE READY FOR A FUN DAY AT THE SHOPS!
CAN YOU FIT THEIR NAMES AND THE SHOPPIE WORDS INTO THE GRID?

B
S
P

JESSICAKE
POPETTE
DONATINA
BUBBLEISHA
PEPPAMINT
SHOP
BESTIES
DREAM

# PHOTOBOMB!

WHICH SILLY SHOPKINS HAVE SNEAKED INTO THE SHOPPIES' SELFIE?
WRITE THEIR NAMES HERE!

1 _____ _____
2 _____ ____
3 _____
4 _____ _____
5 _____ ____

# SMALL MART RACE

The Fruit & Veg gang have decided to have a race! Who will make it across the store and back to their aisle first?

PLAY this board game to find out!

START

**1**

**2**

**3**
Bread Head stops you for a chat. Miss a turn.

**17**

**16**

**15**

**14**

**13**
BAKERY

**18**

**19**

**20**
Frost T Fridge wants to chill out. Miss a turn.

**21**

FINISH
FRUIT & VEG

**32**

**31**
HOMEWARES

**30**
Zappy Microwave shares a speedy trick. Move forward 3 spaces.

# HOW TO PLAY

- Use Shopkins Fruit & Veg characters as your counters.
- Find a dice and roll it to begin. Whoever gets the highest number starts.
- Take turns rolling the dice and moving that number of squares across the board.
- If you land on a marked square, follow the directions.
- Whoever gets to the Fruit & Veg aisle first is the winner!

**4**

**5**

**6**

**7**

**8**

**12**

**11**

**10** Mary Meringue distracts another player. Jump ahead 3 spaces.

**9 SWEET TREATS**

**15**

**22** Al Foil shows you a short cut. Move on 2 spaces.

**23 PANTRY**

**24**

**25**

**29**

**28** Uh-oh, you slip on Ice Cream Dream's spill. Move back 4 spaces.

**27**

**26**

# MEET SEASON 3

## PEACHY
She always gives you a warm, fuzzy feeling when you meet her.

♥s chillin' out with Ice Cream Dream.

## SWEET PEA
Cute and cosy, and ready to pop out of their pod.

♥s juggling.

## BAKERY

## CHEESE LOUISE
A cool little mover. When it comes to being smooth, she takes the cake!

♥s telling cheesy jokes to her friends.

## PATTY CAKE
A real frost-top who loves to sprinkle joy wherever she goes.

♥s speed-baking!

## TOASTIE BREAD
Warm at heart with a very dry sense of humour.

♥s surprising Toasty Pop when he least expects it!

## SWEET TREATS

## SUZIE SUNDAE
She's nuts about ice cream and can whip up a yummy treat in seconds.

♥s relaxing on a sundae.

## MACCA ROON
A bit of an airhead, but one of the sweetest Shopkins you'll ever meet.

♥s getting a new colour put in!

## CANDY APPLE
When she starts something, she sticks with it.

♥s playing fiddle sticks.

## INTERNATIONAL FOOD

## TACO TERRIE
This Tex Mex is full of beans and can go a bit over the top!

♥s dancing around sombreros.

## NETTI SPAGHETTI
Long and thin, and she loves to spin!

♥s twirling in ballet classes.

## CHATTER
Loves to have a chat and
is a very good listener.

♥s talking, talking, talking.

## FROST T FRIDGE
A cool chic who loves to chill out, but
can get a little frosty sometimes.

♥s making icy poles.

## STATIONERY

## PENNY PENCIL
Always has a point to make
and likes to leave her mark.

♥s writing and drawing.

## ERICA ERASER
A real problem solver who
loves to right wrongs.

♥s performing magic –
to make things disappear!

## SECRET SALLY
Trustworthy and faithful, she
will always keep your secrets.

♥s playing hide and secret!

## SHOES

## SNEAKY SALLY
A real sneaky mover with a bouncy personality.

♥s being a step ahead of her friends.

## JENNIFER RAYNE
Always up to her ankles in trouble,
and loves to splash out on her friends.

♥s splashing in puddles.

## HATS

## CASPER CAP
The Shopkin who can cap off any outfit
and is always in peak condition.

♥s playing baseball.

## TAYLOR RAYNE
A little wet behind the ears, but very loyal.
She'll always cover for you!

♥s splashing in puddles.

LIMITED EDITION

## ROXY RING

Always has a sparkle in her eye
and is a cut above the rest.

💙 s attending weddings.

## RING-A-ROSIE

Likes to get attached.
Once she's on your finger,
she won't let go.

💙 s playing piano.

## TICKY TOCK

It takes time to get to know
her, but once you do, the
seconds will fly by.

💙 s watching time go by.

## CHELSEA CHARM

Has a strong heart and will be
your bestie forever.

💙 s hanging with her BFF.

## RUBY EARRING

A stylish earring who hangs out
with the beautiful people.

💙 s having lobes of fun!

## BRENDA BROOCH

Likes to be worn, but she never looks
tired. She shines at any occasion.

💙 s dinner parties with friends.

# EXCLUSIVES

## HEELY

Loves to walk the catwalk, but her real dream is to make it big in shoe-biz!

♥s going to the theatre.

## KELLY JELLY

Enjoys hotfooting it to the beach on a sunny day to feel the sand between her straps.

♥s walking on the beach.

## MINDY MIRROR

Always in a reflective mood, she's compact but has a big personality.

♥s checking herself out!

## BLUSHY BRUSH

She may always turn red, but she is very good at covering up how she really feels.

♥s brushing up on her dance lessons.

## WALLY WATER

He likes to be crystal clear when explaining things. A real cool dude!

♥s doing triathlons.

## KYLIE CONE

Can waffle on for hours about how cool she is, but becomes a mess when the heat is on!

♥s snowball fights.

## QUILTY BOOT

Likes to live life in the fast lane but she's really made for style rather than speed.

♥s snuggling up in front of a fireplace.

## PENNY PURSE

Some Shopkins think she's made of money but she's a real penny pincher.

♥s counting her pennies.

# SHOPKIN YOURSELF!

Wouldn't you just LOVE to create your own Shopkin?
Try it now with this super-fun game.

## WHAT WOULD BE YOUR SHOP HANGOUT?

| PANTRY | SHOES | CLEANING & LAUNDRY | HOMEWARES |
|---|---|---|---|
| GO TO A | GO TO B | GO TO C | GO TO D |

## A — WHICH COLOUR IS CUTEST?

| GO TO 1 | GO TO 2 | GO TO 3 | GO TO 4 |
|---|---|---|---|

## B — CHOOSE THE COOLEST SYMBOL.

| GO TO 5 | GO TO 6 | GO TO 7 | GO TO 8 |
|---|---|---|---|

## C — WHICH CHARACTER MAKES YOU MELT?

| GO TO 9 | GO TO 10 | GO TO 11 | GO TO 12 |
|---|---|---|---|

## D — WHICH SHOPPING CARRIER IS BEST?

| GO TO 13 | GO TO 14 | GO TO 15 | GO TO 16 |
|---|---|---|---|

# USE YOUR IMAGINATION AND FILL IN THE FIRST NAME OF YOUR VERY OWN TEENY-TINY SHOPKIN!

**1** _____ Sauce

**2** _____ Biscuit

**3** _____ Herb

**4** _____ Sugar

**5** _____ Sandal

**6** _____ Trainer

**7** _____ Laces

**8** _____ Pump

**9** _____ Squeegee

**10** _____ Duster

**11** _____ Scrubby

**12** _____ Sponge

**13** _____ Heater

**14** _____ Desk

**15** _____ Juicer

**16** _____ Dryer

## NOW DRAW WHAT YOUR ADORABLE SHOPKIN CHARACTER LOOKS LIKE!

# STYLE THE SHOPPIES

Dress up the Shoppies to match their personalities! Add some designs and patterns and then colour them cute.

## POPETTE

A BOWL LOTTA FUN! LOUD AND LOVEABLE, IF THERE'S A CAMERA AROUND, POPETTE WILL POP UP! MOVIES ARE THIS SHOPPIE'S LIFE.

## JESSICAKE

LIFE'S A PIECE OF CAKE FOR THIS LITTLE SWEETIE! SMART, SENSIBLE AND ALWAYS TASTEFULLY DRESSED, SHE LOVES A SHOPPING DAY.

# BUBBLEISHA

WITH A SWEET 'N' SOUR PERSONALITY, THIS GIRL CAN REALLY BURST YOUR BUBBLE. SHE CAN GET INTO STICKY SITUATIONS, BUT IS REALLY AS SWEET AS CANDY.

# PEPPA-MINT

SHE MAY LOOK CHILLED BUT PEPPA-MINT IS ALWAYS HAVING MELTDOWNS! MAYBE SHE KEEPS LOSING HER COOL BECAUSE SHE'S SO WARM HEARTED!

# No Pain, No Gain

**Cheeky Chocolate is on a mission!** He's running on the conveyor belt at the Small Mart checkout as fast as he can. But why?

"Hey Cheeky," calls **Suzie Sundae**, "I think you're, like, running in the wrong direction."

"I'm training for the Shopkins Olympics!" shouts Cheeky.
Cheeky wants to be the marathon champion of Shopville!

**Toasty Pops** has other ideas.

"I'm way faster than you, Cheeky," he says. "I can toast a bagel in ten seconds flat!"

"Uh, I don't know if that's, like, the same thing, Toasty," replies Suzie.

Cheeky Chocolate doesn't think Toasty can ever beat him. He challenges Toasty to a race! **Milk Bud** decides to join in too, just for fun. The Shopkins line up on the conveyor belts, and Suzie prepares to start the race. The last Shopkin standing will be the winner.

"Um, like, go!" Suzie calls.

The conveyor belts rumble around and Cheeky and Toasty start running. Cheeky has a sneaky idea. He grabs a dog treat from the conveyor belt and throws it towards Toasty.

"Fetch!" he calls. Milk Bud spots the treat and jumps for it … landing on top of Toasty and knocking him over!

"Yes! I am the marathon champion!" shouts Cheeky.

Toasty jumps over next to Cheeky's conveyor belt. He picks up a checkout divider and drops it in front of Cheeky.

"Woa, Toasty, what are you doing?" says Cheeky.

"I'm making you the hurdle champion, too," says Toasty, with a smile.

Cheeky can't keep up and trips over the hurdle and crashes into a bucket on the floor.

"You deserve to be the champ, Cheeky," says Toasty. "No pain, no gain!"

The Shopkins all giggle – apart from Cheeky!

## CHECK YA LATER!

# HOMEWARE REPAIR

These awesome Shopkins need some close-up repairs.
Can you match the characters to their names?

**1** **2** **3** **4**

BRENDA BLENDER          VICKY VAC

TOASTY POP          FROST T FRIDGE

# BABY NAMES

Aw, too cute! Can you unscramble the names of these
Baby Shopkins? Then match them to their pictures.

**1** PABBYFUF _ _ _ _ _ _ _ _ _    **3** BIRDSELB _ _ _ _ _ _ _ _

**2** DEPANPYE _ _ _ _ _ _ _ _    **4** SSYPPPIIS _ _ _ _ _ _ _ _ _

**5** YBWABESIPS _ _ _ _ _ _ _ _ _ _

**a**          **b**          **c**          **d**          **e**

ANSWERS ON PAGE 61

# SMALL MART CHECKOUT

Who's the missing character in each row?

# EGGCHIC FOR REAL

Which picture is the real Eggchic?
All of the others have had some pretty strange changes!

## FRUIT & VEG

### APRIL APRICOT

Fun and fruity, but trouble follows her and she usually ends up in a jam.

♥s ripening!

### CHEEKY CHERRIES

Cheeky and cheery, when they put their heads together they can do anything!

♥s finishing off each other's sentences.

## BAKERY

### BAGEL BILLY

Not just a roll with a hole!
He's bagelicious and always filling good.

♥s letting the good times roll!

### ICE CREAM QUEEN

Never cold to her loyal followers, she likes to sprinkle her friendship around.

♥s practicing her Royal 'Wafer'.

### PANCAKE JAKE

A stack of fun and totally pantastic! Will flip over backwards to help you out.

♥s playing Frisbee.

## SWEET TREATS

### BERRY SMOOTHIE

A real smooth mover who's all glass and knows how to blend into a crowd.

♥s helping smooth out problems.

## COMFY CHAIR

An easy chair to get along with and always comfortable to be around.

♥ s being a big softy.

## TAMMY TV

Wide-eyed and excited, always loud – until someone turns down her volume.

♥ s being the centre of attention.

# ACCESSORIES

# GARDEN

## HANDBAG HARRIET

A little cutie who can handle anything. Loves to get carried away!

♥ s carrying on with her friends.

## PETA PLANT

A real head for gardening. She has a hair-do that's blooming marvellous!

♥ s lazing in the sun!

# PARTY TIME

## JUNE BALLOON

Never flat and always the life of the party. So happy she could burst!

♥ s decorating.

## MISS PRESSY

With the gift of the gab, this generous Shopkin is the gift that just keeps giving.

♥ s party invites and keeping wishes secret.

# PETSHOP

## GOLDIE FISH BOWL

A really busy bowl who sometimes finds it hard to keep her head above the water.

♥ s deep sea diving.

**LIMITED EDITION**

## PRETTY PUFF

Always on the go, she's super
fit and never gets puffed out.

♥s spreading her sweet scent.

## PRETTY BOW KAY

This little cutie looks as pretty
as she smells.

♥s spraying the day away.

## FRENCHY PERFUME

Oh La La! A true romantic who always
dreams of living in Paris.

♥s sharing breakfast with Croissant d'Or.

## SPARKLY SPRITZ

A glamorous Shopkin with
a sparkly personality.

♥s filling the air with pretty scents.

## GEMMA BOTTLE

A cut above the rest! She
always shines when she steps
out on the town.

♥s the sweet smell of success.

## SALLY SCENT

A real sweetheart of a perfume
who can be a little self-scented.

♥s playing match maker!

# PETKINS

**MILK BUD**

A real moosic lover who never cries when she spills herself.

♥ s making moosic!

**BONE-ADETTE**

A funny bone who's always yappy, except when she's buried by her doggy friends!

♥ s visiting the butcher shop.

**EGGCHIC**

A house for a real high flyer and the best nest in town.

♥ s his 'home tweet home'!

**RITA REMOTE**

A little short-tempered so don't press her buttons!

♥ s changing her tune.

**JADE SPADE**

A Shopkin who really digs gardening. It's dirty job but someone has to do it!

♥ s spending hours in the garden.

**HOT CHOC**

Warm and welcoming, she's a great friend to finish off the night with.

♥ s camping.

**SHY PIE/CHERRY PIE**

Cherry nice and ready to slice, this is a Shopkin you can always 'crust'.

♥ s being a cutie pie.

**FISH FLAKE JAKE**

Gets a bit shaky when he's around gold fish but is always happy to share at dinnertime.

♥ s sharing his talents.

**DRIPS**

Can be silly and very spilly! Fill him with water and watch him grow.

♥ s to help in the garden.

**JINGLE PURSE**

Only has a few coins to her name, but is rich with friends.

♥ s being a real mover and shaker.

# YOU + ME = BEST FRIENDS

## FRIEND FILE FOR YOU

### ABOUT ME

Favourite colour: _____

A word/phrase I use ALL the time: _____

_____

Favourite hobby: _____

I would love to be a: _____

Favourite Shopkin: _____

Because _____

Favourite Petkin: _____

Because _____

My favourite Shoppie is: _____

Because _____

### ABOUT MY BFF

Favourite colour: _____

A word/phrase he/she uses ALL the time: _____

Favourite hobby: _____

He/she would love to be a: _____

Favourite Shopkin: _____

Because _____

Favourite Petkin: _____

Because _____

My favourite Shoppie is: _____

Because _____

Make sure this page is covered when your friend fills in her side. No cheeky peeks!

Friendship is super important to the Shopkins. How well do you and your BFF know each other? Take turns to fill out one side of this friend file each and then check your match-up success!

# FRIEND FILE FOR YOUR FRIEND

## ABOUT MY BFF

Favourite colour: _____

A word/phrase he/she uses ALL the time: _____
_____

Favourite hobby: _____

He/she would love to be a: _____

Favourite Shopkin: _____

Because _____

Favourite Petkin: _____

Because _____

My favourite Shoppie is: _____

Because _____

## ABOUT ME

Favourite colour: _____

A word/phrase I use ALL the time: _____

Favourite hobby: _____

I would love to be a: _____

Favourite Shopkin: _____

Because _____

Favourite Petkin: _____

Because _____

My favourite Shoppie is: _____

Because _____

Now check your answers and see how many match-ups you get!

ANSWERS ON PAGE 61

# MATCHING BUDDIES

The Shopkins are all mixed up! None of the characters are sitting next to their doubles. Can you draw lines to pair up the buddies?

Which character doesn't have a match?

# SHOPPIES SPOTTING

## PEPPA-MINT AND THE OTHER SHOPPIES ARE HAVING AN AMAZING DAY OUT WITH THEIR SHOPKIN BFFS!

# THESE SEASON 4 SHOPKINS HAVE SNEAKED INTO THE SCENE. CAN YOU SPOT THEM?

CAN YOU FIND THESE LITTLE PICTURES IN THE BIG SCENE? TICK THEM AS YOU FIND THEM.

1

2

3

4

5

6

# ARE YOU A SHOPKINS SUPER-FAN?

**How well do you know your fave Shopkins? Try this quiz to find out!**

**1** Which of these characters is not a Shopkin?
a. Swiss Miss
b. Petra Porridge
c. Lennie Lime

**2** Which character belongs in the Health & Beauty aisle?
a. Scrubs
b. Sizzles
c. Peachy

**3** Which aisle does Dippy Avocado belong in?
a. Fruit & Veg
b. Pantry
c. Sweet Treats

**4** What's the name of the butter Shopkin?
a. Barry Butter
b. Butterfly
c. Buttercup

**5** Which Shopkin should not be in the Party Food aisle?
a. Wishes
b. Cheezey B
c. Berry Smoothie

**6** Which character belongs in the Sweet Treats aisle?
a. Papa Tomato
b. Snow Crush
c. Candy Kisses

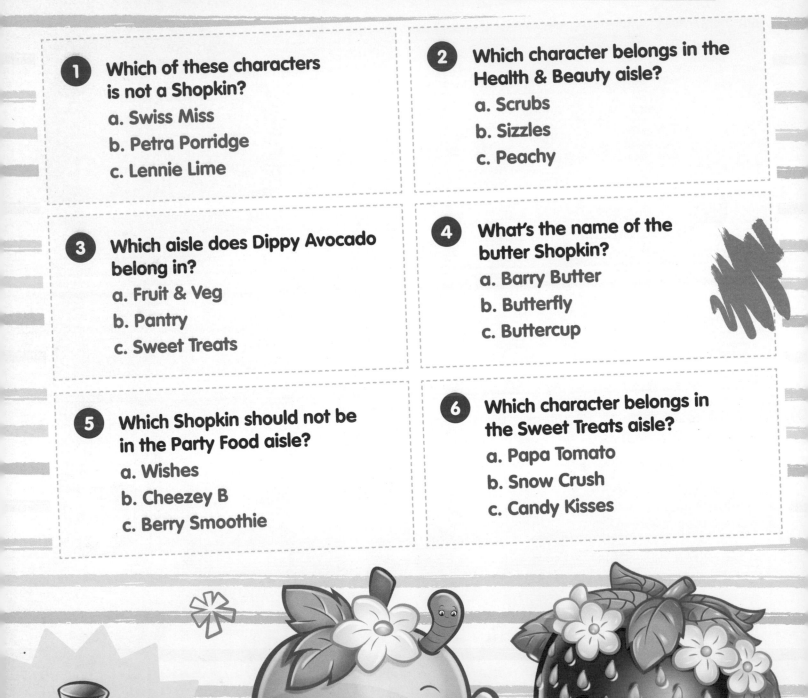

**7** Which of these characters is not a Petkin?
a. Jade Spade
b. Tina Treats
c. Hot Choc

**8** What colours does Milk Bud come in?
a. Pink and blue
b. Purple and blue
c. Pink and white

**9** Which aisle does Kelly Jelly belong in?
a. Sweet Treats
b. Bakery
c. Shoes

**10** What's the name of the jam Shopkin?
a. Gran Jam
b. Jerry Jam
c. Sugar Lump

**11** Which character belongs in the Petshop aisle?
a. Goldie Fish Bowl
b. Googy
c. Miss Mushy Moo

**12** Which character belongs in the Bakery aisle?
a. Silky
b. Patty Cake
c. Chloe Flower

**13** What's the name of the bagel Shopkin?
a. Bagel Brenda
b. Billy Bagel
c. Bagel Billy

**14** Which aisle does Taylor Rayne belong in?
a. Hats
b. Shoes
c. Homewares

**15** What's the name of the watering can Petkin?
a. Molly Mops
b. Chatter
c. Drips

**16** Which character is a Season 4 Limited Edition?
a. Ruby Earring
b. Roxie Ring
c. Sally Scent

# NOW CHECK YOUR ANSWERS THEN TURN OVER THE PAGE TO FIND OUT YOUR RESULTS!

# QUIZ RESULTS!

## 0-6
## SHOPKINS STARTER

You have a bag-full of Shopkins swotting to do before you can be a real super-fan. Try reading back through the 'Meet the Shopkins' pages in this book. You'll be an expert of the aisles in no time!

## 7-11
## COOL COLLECTOR

You're definitely a regular visitor to Shopville with all those correct answers – but you have a few more things to tick off your shopping list. Spend some more time with the Shopkins and who knows what's in store!

## 12-16
## SHOPKINS SUPER-FAN!

Decorate the aisles and make an announcement in store – you're a Shopkins expert! Bet you have a trolley-load of your favourite characters lining the shelves.
Keep it up, you've got the ultimate shopping style.

YOU'RE ALL WINNERS – LIKE ME!

ANSWERS ON PAGE 61

# CATCH THE PETKINS

How quickly can you find all 10 Season 4 Petkins in the grid?
Set your watch and time yourself – ticking them as you go.

CAN YOUR FRIENDS BEAT YOUR TIME? HEE, HEE!

# MY SHOPKINS STORY

Do you love hearing what the Shopkins are up to in the aisles?
Now you can write your own teeny tale!

## SEE HOW MANY OF THESE CHARACTERS YOU CAN FIT IN YOUR STORY:

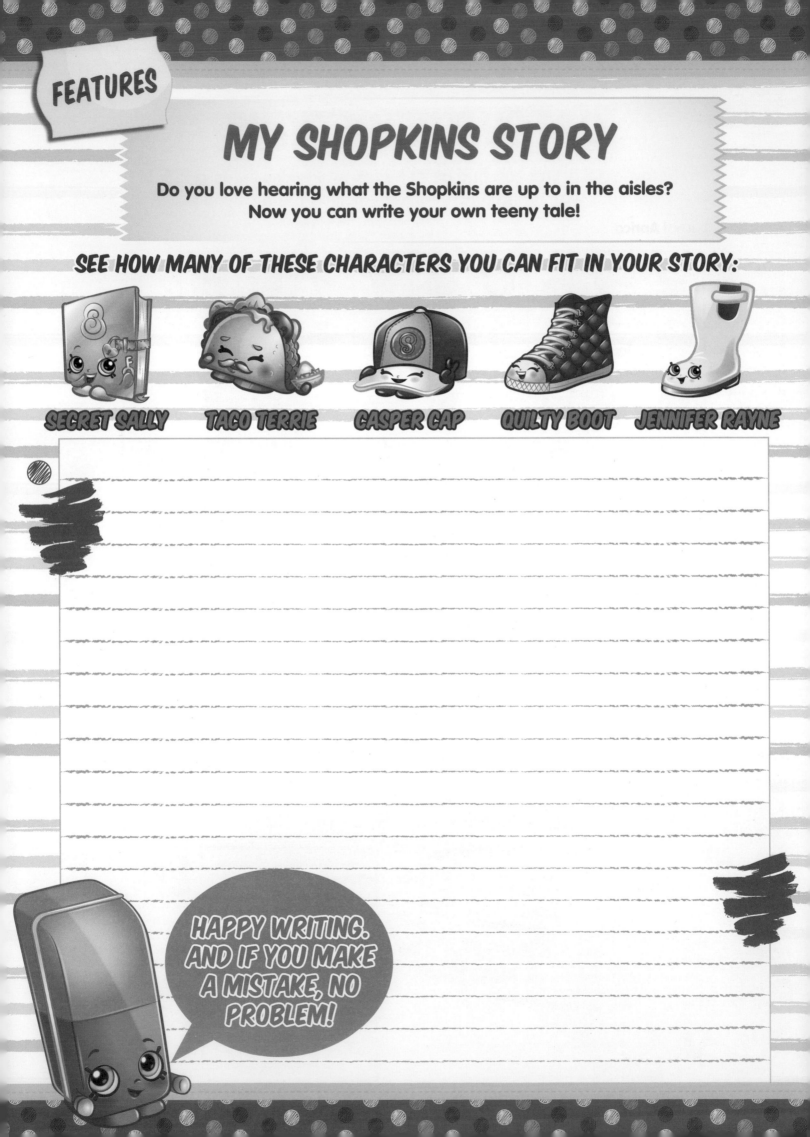

**SECRET SALLY**    **TACO TERRIE**    **CASPER CAP**    **QUILTY BOOT**    **JENNIFER RAYNE**

HAPPY WRITING.
AND IF YOU MAKE
A MISTAKE, NO
PROBLEM!

# ANSWERS

## PAGES 8-9

**Blind Bag:** 1. April Apricot,
2. Cheeky Cherries, 3. Peachy,
4. Dippy Avocado, 5. Posh Pear,
6. Apple Blossom.

**Mystery Shopkin:** Juicy Orange.

**Shopkins Shadows:** 1. Taco Terrie,
2. Sneaky Sally, 3. Taylor Rayne,
4. Penny Purse, 5. Blushy Brush
6. Roxy Ring.

**Aisle Be Quick:**

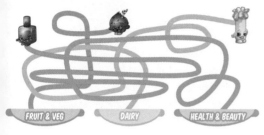

FRUIT & VEG    DAIRY    HEALTH & BEAUTY

## PAGE 18

**Fruit & Veg:** Posh Pear, Miss
Mushy Moo, Corny Cob, Silly
Chilli, April Apricot; **Party Food:**
Soda Pops, Wishes, Rainbow
Bite; **Bakery:** Patty Cake, Toastie
Bread, Bagel Billy, Mini Muffin.

**The Shopkin that doesn't belong
is Fasta Pasta.**

## PAGE 27

The missing Shopkins are:
Corny Cob, Mini Muffin,
Tommy Ketchup, Mindy Mirror
and Snow Crush.

## PAGE 28

Real: 1, 3, 5, 6;
Fake: 2, 4, 7, 8.

## PAGE 29

1. Chatter, 2. Al Foil,
3. Macca Roon, 4. Leafy

| | | | | | | | | | |
|---|---|---|---|---|---|---|---|---|---|
| J | A | T | R | O | L | L | E | Y | B |
| T | S | Z | A | L | F | O | I | L | A |
| I | U | I | S | V | I | M | P | L | G |
| L | T | P | A | N | T | R | Y | E | C |
| L | S | T | O | C | K | V | V | A | H |
| B | A | K | E | R | Y | Q | Q | F | A |
| R | A | I | B | N | K | Z | Q | Y | T |
| M | A | C | C | A | R | O | O | N | T |
| C | H | E | C | K | O | U | T | Y | E |
| D | A | I | R | Y | U | W | V | Q | R |

## PAGES 30-31

**Petkin match: Donatina: Daisy
Donut, Rolly Donut; Jessicake:
Cherry Cake, Coco Cupcake;
Popette: Bowl-inda Popcorn,
Polly Popcorn; Bubbleisha:
Bubblicious, Gumball Gabby;
Peppa-Mint: Icy-Bowl,
Carla Cone.**

**Girls' day out:**

**Photobomb!:** 1. Handbag Harriet,
2. Sippy Sips, 3. Prommy,
4. Lolli Poppins, 5. Fairy Crumbs.

## PAGES 44-45

**Homeware Repair:** 1. Vicky Vac,
2. Frost T Fridge, 3. Toasty Pop,
4. Brenda Blender.

**Baby Names:** 1. Baby Puff,
2. Nappy Dee, 3. Dribbles,
4. Sippy Sips, 5. Baby Swipes.

**Small Mart Checkout:**
1. c, 2. a, 3. b.

**Eggchic for Real:**
4 is the real Eggchic.

## PAGE 52

**Scrubs doesn't have a match.**

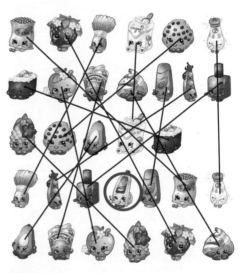

## PAGE 55

## PAGE 59